What are nurdl

A nurdle is a very small plastic pellet
Billions are used every year to make most o......... products.
Many of them end up in the sea and are washing up on shorelines around the world.
I wrote this story when I started finding them on the beaches that I love.

The nurdles and plastics pictured in this book
have all been collected during my beach cleans.

This book is dedicated to my amazing Nan,
Elizabeth Fortune James

First published in the UK in 2020 by Peahen Publishing Ltd
www.peahenpublishing.com

Copyright © 2020 Seaborn Design

Designed and Illustrated by Jo Joof

ISBN: 978-1-8381099-0-5

A CIP catalogue record for this is available
from the British Library

Paper sourced from sustainable forests

Peahen
Publishing

Nurdle

love
Claire Vowell
and Nurdle
xxx

Written by Claire Vowell
Illustrated and designed by Jo Joof

Hi, my name is Nurdle.
Can you see me?

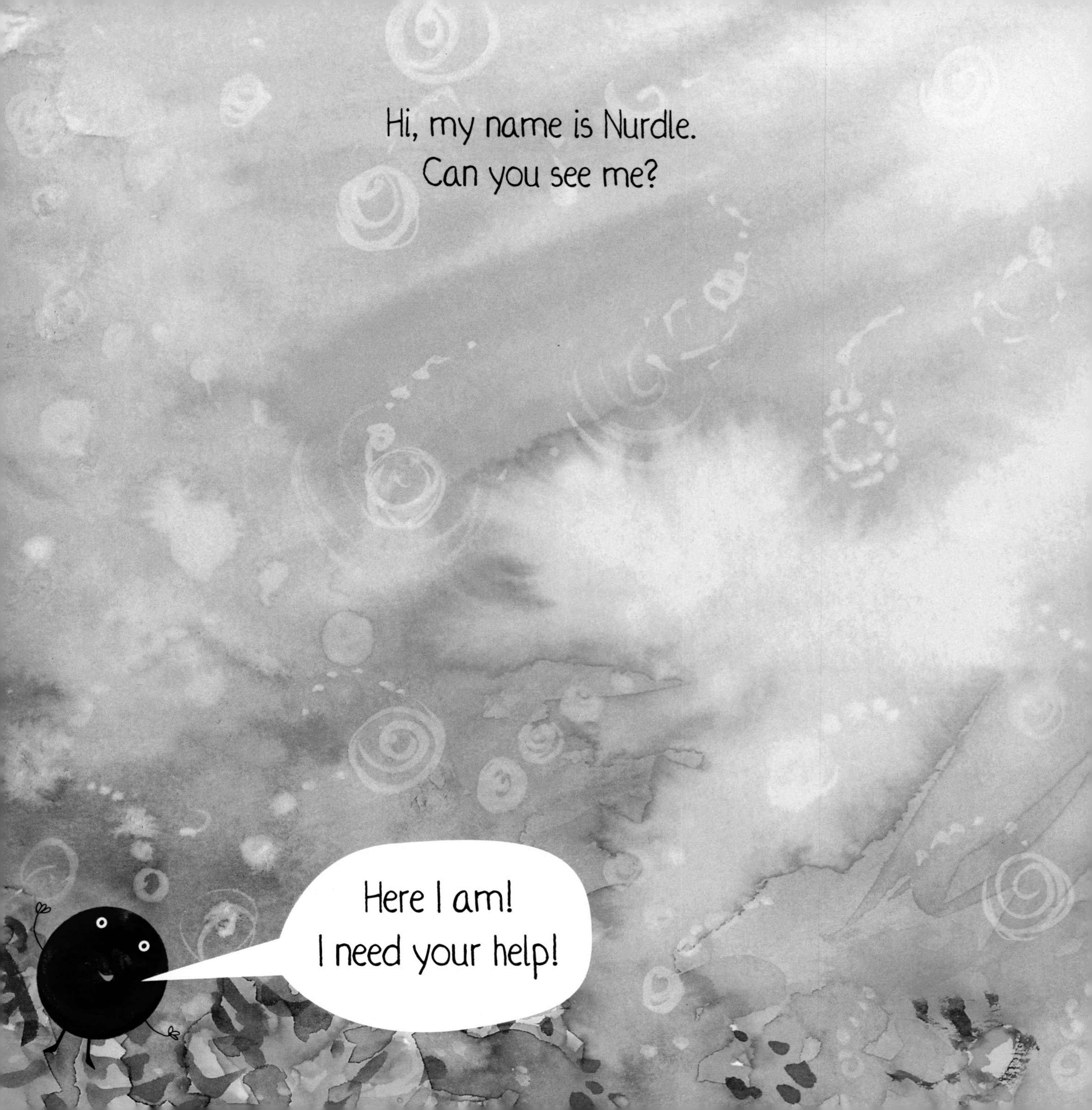

I'm teeny and tiny, friendly and gentle.
A pellet of plastic, the size of a lentil.

My family's made up of millions and millions.

My friends round the world number billions and billions!

But all of us nurdles are feeling quite sad,
'cos everyone says that we're mean and we're bad.

They say that we're destroying the earth and the sea,
but this isn't our fault, as I hope you'll agree.

We nurdles just wanted to make your life good —
we're lighter than metal, we're lighter than wood.

We're easy to move, melt and shape,
but we're small and slippy and accidentally escape.

We end up like crumbs on the factory floor.
They then call us dirty — no use anymore.

So they sweep us away, send us off to landfill,
or hose us down gutters and drainpipes until ...

We float through rivers, past houses and trees,
and eventually end up afloat in the seas.

Which was never the place we intended to be.

A nurdle is NOT meant to be in the sea!

Sometimes we escape when we're out on the roads,
transported in lorries, boxed up in big loads,

and if we slip free, we can pour out in piles.
If we're not swept up, we can travel for miles!

We don't walk on legs or wear nurdle shoes,
but there's hundreds of ways that nurdles can move!

We're light as a feather, we dance on the air,
into fields, into ditches, and once we're out there ...

If not eaten by animals or lost on the ground,

we return to the sea, bobbing around.

Once in the sea we nurdles can float,
get mistaken for food and swim down a throat!

But nurdles in tummies
cause tummies to fill,

so the creatures stop eating,
and get really ill.

Some nurdles absorb oil when floating at sea,
which makes us more toxic and brings misery.

After years in the ocean, we wash up ashore.
We're glad to be back on the dry land once more.

When piles and piles of us land on a beach,
we cause still more trouble on shores that we reach.

We look just like fish eggs from a bird's eye view,
so they gobble us down and get poorly too.

But we nurdles don't do this for fun.
We were man-made to improve life for everyone!

We dream of being useful, with a long, long life.
And becoming something special, not harming wildlife!

So we need YOUR help. It would be really fantastic,
if you joined us in the fight against single-use plastic!

The less plastic you use, the less nurdles get free,

polluting the land and the rivers and sea.

Let's stop single usage. Yes, that's a great plan!
Re-use and recycle whenever you can.

Help clean up the beaches and rivers and land,
and search out my nurdle friends lost in the sand.

Whether you're old or young, tiny or tall,

let's make this Earth of ours special for all!

We nurdles of the world thank you for caring!

HELP THE NURDLES!

If Nurdle has inspired you to do a beach clean, or to collect nurdles, please wear gloves and wash your hands carefully afterwards.
Keep the nurdles you find in a jam jar and share their story with your friends, or place them in a bin, as sadly nurdles cannot be recycled.
For more information about nurdles and The Great Nurdle Hunt go to

Nurdlehunt.org.uk.

Have fun, stay safe and love our amazing world.
Love Claire x